quarantine and everything

after

-maggie belle

D1305993

for: the people who changed my life, you know who you

are. i love you

## table of contents

**before you begin**

this book is a collection of moments. starting

from the beginning of quarantine i found myself craving

a way to get creative; all my distractions were gone and

i found myself alone with my thoughts. you'll find these

small moments broken up into three categories. the first

being isolation. poems and prose were written from my

darkest thoughts, my reminiscing, and my hopes for the

future when the world returns to normal. this section is

sad and mournful. next is freedom. stories of my life

before quarantine, realizations i had in isolation, and

reflections on memories i made once i got out. this

section is the happiest of the three, diving deep into my

subconscious to pick apart the moments and memories

that are important to me so that i could hang on to those

feelings forever. finally, we have love. the largest section

of the bunch. this section contains stories of heartbreak,

lust, love, toxicity, and happiness. unlike the rest of the

sections, this one contains many stories that are not my

own. i wrote through new perspectives, basing these

moments on stories that i've heard from my closest

friends, and some that i have completely fantasized.

some are my own but the majority are based on

someone in my life or a story i came up with. this section

is filled with all kinds of emotion that i cannot tell you

how you will feel while reading. if you picked up my little

book, thank you. enjoy a deep dive into my psyche.

welcome.

# isolation

**the world was never ours**
and in these times of uncertainty and scare we are
reminded of our own morality
the world is reminded of the pain and suffering that
comes with being a human being
regardless of the technology advances, wars, and
seemingly perfect lives
we are nothing but cells with a conscience
if something so small can take out the globe
why are we trying to do the same to each other?

**the fuel to my nightmares**
i'm trying to be happy. pretend this is okay.
like a bad dream that will be over soon.
but i can't be happy when a small tiny virus has taken
everything i love
i feel like i'm dying.
falling into a descent of insanity.
from being home and being alone.
i was finally happy. but now i don't know.
i don't want to be dramatic. act overly privileged.
but i'm scared and sad and alone again.
i'm stuck in my own head and i can't get out.

**sooner or later**
and now may we never fail to appreciate
the eye of a stranger
an embrace with a lover
a moment with a friend

may when we return have a new love for
a class in school
a meeting at work
a difficult practice

may we learn to care for
those who need our help
those we chose to ignore
those who have done us wrong

for i don't know when
life will start again
but i can hold on to the hope

that i will see you all
this will all be over
the world will be restored
soon.

**take me back to the start**
i used to complain
that the the candescent lights
used to hurt my eyes
but it's nothing compared to
the pain of computer screens
and one dimensional classmates
that i once thought were annoying
i wish i could go back
to classrooms with white light
to the kids who talked to much
because i took for granted
all i had

**what would you change if you could?**
if i had known that, that friday would be the last day of
my junior year. i would have been happier.

if i had know that, that friday would be the last day i saw
my teachers for months. i would have hugged them.

if i had known that, that friday would be the last classes
with my senior friends. i would have told them i love
them.

if i had known that, that friday would be the last lunch
with my girls. i would have treated them.

if i had known that, that tuesday would have been my
last practice with my team. i would have worked harder.

if i had known that, that tuesday would be my last time
to touch a ball in months. i wouldn't have looked at the
clock.

if i had known that, that saturday would be my last day
at work. i would have cleaned more.

**what would you change if you could? continued**
if i had known that my entire life would be uprooted just
as it was getting better, I would have cherished the
moments that i had in my favorite places. i would have
hugged the people that made my life amazing. i would
have given my all and lived those days like they were
my last. because in a sense they were. and i hope and
pray i can have my world back and when i do i will live
each day like a global pandemic could take it away
tomorrow.

**some divine plan**
and maybe we were never meant to see
what could've been without the world ending
the way our lives would have progressed without our
newfound strength
the memories or creativity
the relationships we built and the ones we found didn't
matter anymore
the shallow pools we were swimming in became deep
holes of prosperity we never knew we needed
so i don't think we were ever meant to see
what could have been because without the world ending
our lives would have never changed

**don't let me grow up**
i applied to college today
and i still feel like a junior
and it's hard for me to understand
that if i ever go back to school
things won't be the same

i applied to college today
and i likely will never experience
high school prom
a final homecoming
a senior run or pep rally

i applied to college today
and i know i should be happy
but i feel so somber
because i only got five real months
of high school

i applied to college today
and i know if i ever go back
it won't be the same
smiles behind masks
six feet between us

**don't let me grow up continued**
i applied to college today
and i'll never get to be a part
of the senior class
that when a freshman sees us
they think "i can't wait"

i applied to college today
and i am sad
my last few months of childhood
were robbed by a virus and politics
but they say i can't be selfish

i applied to college today
and i hope by then this is over
and i hope i get a senior year
even if it's just one day
back at my favorite place

i applied to college today
and i feel uneasy
i hope i can say a proper goodbye
to my childhood to my school
and hopefully stop mourning
my senior year

**will this ever end?**
remember when it was april 6th?
april 20th?
april 30th?
next year for sure.
september 8th?
october 16th?
hopefully next semester.
please stop crying.

what if my life wasn't made up of
half experienced
where when things get good
they disappear
into my own little figment
but relax people are dying.

my eyes burn from the screens
and my head hurts from the tears
my lungs burn from the masks
and my heart hurts from the memories
please stop crying.

the days seem to slip away
into the same mundane routine
eating lunch alone
virtual classes with no learning
constant sadness
but relax people are dying.

**will this ever end? continued**
it never is easy, i know that
but i thought the world
could give me a break
something that i once adored
has me completely burnt out
please stop crying.

why is this the way
my childhood has to end
i can't be in solitude
overthinking everything
feeling so beaten down
but relax people are dying.

**life is meant for lustful living**
don't fall in love
with people
with places
because everything
good or bad or indifferent
will come to an end

i'm not telling you
to be sad all the time
i'm telling you to live for lust
live for your thrills
but keep your heart in a lockbox

love kills
attachment hurts
remember there is always a catch
even if it seems perfect
nothing ever is

and you may think i'm sadistic
that i'll never find true bliss
that my thrills are too cheap
to be real
and maybe you're right

but for now all i can say
is love will break you and
the world will stop turning
and the few moments of bliss
aren't worth the pain

# freedom

**live for you**
life can either be lived
recklessly or vicariously
actively or passively
the choice is up to you
but memories are not made
in the shadow of another

**new beginnings change everything**
one day something will happen that will change you
forever.
and that might be a small moment.
a person you meet.
or a decision you make.
and for me it was getting out of the car.
it was walking in knowing nobody.
feeling terrified that it wouldn't work again.
but it was the sudden love and warmth that i felt that led
me to stay.
and that moment that changed my life was like any other
day.

**i'll never be her**
tell me what it's like to be a pretty girl.
where you can wake up and put hair in a bun and the
boys still fancy you.
tell me what it's like to be a pretty girl.
the kind of beautiful you know is there.
the type of innocent beauty you see in the movies.
tell me what it's like to be a pretty girl.
to not feel like a stranger to yourself in the mirror
and know all of your imperfections all too well.

**different type of pretty girl**
girls like me don't show up on screens
ringing through your headphones or in between book
pages
but girls like me can see the world
for everything it is and everything it's been
and know there's more to life than the stories that we
see

**my wild side**
i see myself in color
a plethora of pinks and purples
i live my life intensely
fully present in the moment
i fear commitment
i am all i need
and yet people gravitate towards me
the life of the party
confident and charming
living life on the wild side

**my quiet side**
i see myself in black and white
a blurred together color pallet of grey
i live my life quietly
inside the walls of my skull
i long for my person
i don't like myself enough to live in solitude
and yet i'm lonely all the time
the backup friend never on the invite list
smart and shy
living life inside the lines

**four**
we were the teenagers we had seen
on the movie screens
life was moving fast
but we were living it recklessly
the stars shined just for us

**fast lane feelings**
a touch. a song. a kiss.
a moment. a memory of pure bliss.
replaying in my head as i fall asleep
words spoken. air conditioning
talking without the world listening
watching the city at night
the defining little moments that make up my life

**don't waste it**
life in every sense of it is worth living.
your highest highs shows the best the world has to offer
and your lowest lows shows you where to improve.
rock bottom may seem like forever
but rock bottom is only a starting point for the future.
there is beauty in pain and pain in beauty
life is worth it. don't lose it.

**my highway home**
from the cotton candy morning skies
to the quite pitch black nights
i knew this road would have my back
through moments of love and fight
watching all the people
driving just like me
speeding through the fast lane
getting where they need to be
this highway brings me comfort
a fast sort of freedom
and drops me right back at my door
once the day is gone and done

**beauty in brokenness**

and suddenly the world in which she surrounded herself
was one of purity and love.
the walls that once enclosed her
and the fears that once debilitated her
came crumbling down with her perfect reputation.
but to her. finally. that was okay.
and finally the people that she ran to were the ones who
truly care.
and for the first time since forever.
someone actually wanted her there.

**trip to the stars**
there are so many stars i'll never see
people i'll never meet
places i'll never go
but for the first time maybe ever
the people that filled my world
my tiny sweet little world
we're the people that made life worth it
the places i'll never go
the people i'll never meet
the stars i'll never see
don't matter anymore
because the world is far to vast
far to big
and that's okay
i don't have to see the world
i don't have to touch the stars
because my world was what i needed
the universe picked me
to be the person i am
and the stars are mine
i see them in the people i know
the people i love
the stars are mine

# love

**i forgot my raincoat**
you were my summer rain
you drenched me to the core
washed away my painful past
and left me nice and warm
our winter blues were rinsed away
and gave us sparkling skies
stormy nights faded to sweet mornings
crazy how time flies
you cleaned my soul with just one pass
of your soft and simple storm
but when the day break came we found
it wasn't summer anymore

**romantic chaos**
perfect and messy
flawless and wrong
like the summer air rolling through the windows
like the stars watching from the sky
living out our "what ifs"
living out our "what could go wrongs"
faithful and illicit
pure and sinful

**if things were different**
they needed a better place
it was the wrong time
life was getting in the way
she never falls for schoolboys
or the ones on magazines
but this time the stars aligned
when he showed up in her life
the suspense was getting heavy
she was tired of holding on
till he showed up at her house that night
and assured her he was hers
that night changed everything
flipped her whole world on its head
while she wishes for that place and time
she's thankful that her stars aligned

**this isn't love**
she drank his toxic poison
she thought it was the cure
but it was never what she needed
he has her in a chokehold
thinking that it's love
convincing her that she's the problem
that he's a work of god
much too sweet to ever leave
she relies on his venom
till she's just a shell
of the girl she used to be

**seperation**
it's always amazes me
how someone can be mystified by a stranger
and filled with desire
but lose the feeling of lust
once they become a lover
how the want disappears to become one of reliance
once the relation became too much
once they have you they fade away
into the oblivion of comfort and blandness.

**downtown signs**
the city lights shinned for us that night
maybe you don't remember
maybe i was some passing fad
but those lights are burned into my memory
the lights told me to hold on to you
that maybe we would work someday
the twinkle in your eye
the memories that we made
lit by the glow of the city lights
that night was ours
and i am yours

**backseat memories**
and we wonder if they will ever understand just how
important they are to us
just how much they changed the entire trajectory of our
lives
how the memories we have of them live rent free in our
minds
the way the world shined just a little brighter because we
met people who lived their lives just like us
regardless if they know it or not
they changed us

**daydreams**
for years she watched him
his charisma drew her in
she knew he wouldn't want her
at least in that way
but she watched him still
and when they finally got to talking
the pair were two in the same
conversation flowing easy
both with a charming charisma
that only belonged to them
the pair became best friends
and she finally understood
that it was exactly what she wanted
all those years of watching
romanticizing and fantasizing
she finally had a friendship
that was exactly what she needed

**i can't get rid of you**
you're the smoke i can't air out of my favorite sweater
stuck like the blood stain in my carpet from last
november
tattooed on my eyelids as i fall asleep
memories that wash up as moments i couldn't keep
scars from a battlefield i can't remember fighting on
sung in the background vocals of my old favorite song
your name echoes in my ears all night
till the morning reminds me of you in golden daylight

**i was never superstitious**
when 11:11 flashed on my watch
and your name floated into my mind
i knew you were what i wanted
when i can't blow out a candle
without a moment of hesitation
i knew you were what i wanted
when a fallen eyelash on my cheek
had your name interlaced in mascara
i knew you were what i wanted
now all my superstitious became signs of you

**two hearts beating in sync**
silky smooth
soft and sweet
the girl who brought you to your knees
her heart closed off
yours was too
but it was different with her you knew
her eyes matched yours
a cloudy grey
a innocent smile that would never fade
two bodies one brain
everything about you two was the same
rosy and mysterious
pink and shy
she was yours you were her guy

**broken like me**
i never thought that people like me could be loved
that we were worth more than our extrinsic value
that my wounds and scars could be stitched back
together
and then i met you
you weren't just a person like me
you were my other half
the first person to uncover my scars
and lick my wounds
before stitching them back together with golden thread
you showed me that people like us are intrinsically
connected
that people like us can be loved, we can love each other

**alice and her mad hatter**
i don't know if i met you
out of some divine happenstance
or some cosmic plan from the universe
but regardless when you stumbled into my life
while we were both tripping over our own feet
we fell down a rabbit hole
here in wonderland
the night was alive
the universe aligned
in a flawless symphony
you put my chords back in tune
in wonderland it was just me and you
no matter how we met
or why you're in my life
there has to be some greater plan
for us to meet again
down a rabbit hole to wonderland

**till we meet again**
two hearts
attached in the moment
not without fear of the future
but with plans to reunite
his eyes were locked with hers
their fingers intertwined
he knew he had to let her go
but it was too late to say goodbye

Made in the USA
Columbia, SC
21 September 2020

21264253R00026